VocalChoices

VocalChoices

20 key exercises for teachers and their pupils

Liz McNaughton
Matthew Kemp

Foreword by Professor Graham Welch

First published in Great Britain in 2016 by
Phoenix Again (Publishing)
90 Shinfield Road
Reading
Berkshire
RG2 7DA

www.phoenixagain.com

ISBN 978-0-9543165-4-9

A catalogue record for this book is available from the British Library.

ISBN 978-0-9543165-5-6 (epub)

ISBN 978-0-9543165-6-3 (mobi)

Web link for video and exercise templates: www.vocalchoices.com

Cover design, book design and layout, and anatomical drawings by Reuben McNaughton

Printed in the UK by YPS (York Publishing Services) www.yps-publishing.co.uk

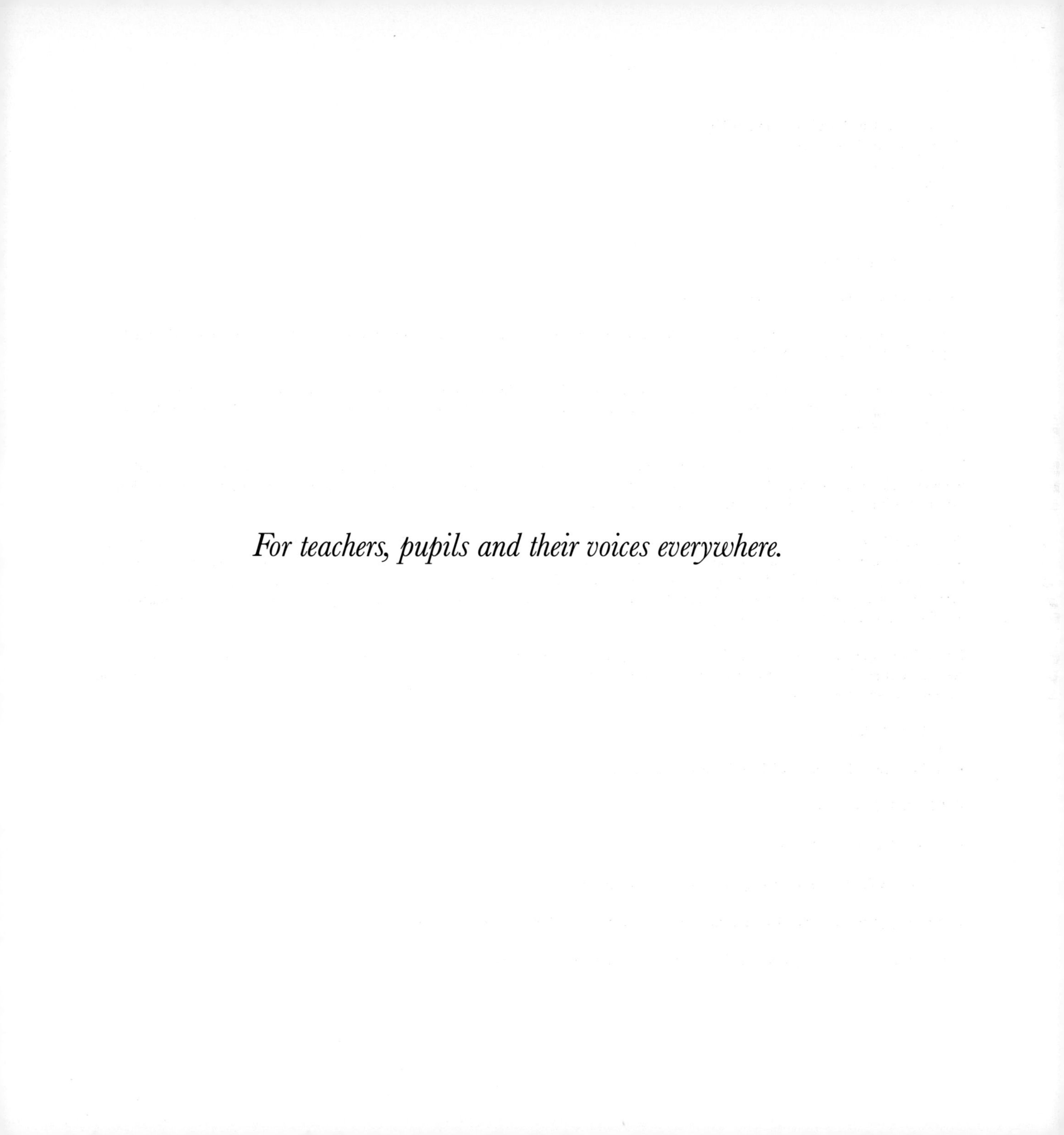

For teachers, pupils and their voices everywhere.

Contents

List of figures

Web link for video and exercise templates: www.vocalchoices.com

Acknowledgements

For enthusiasm, encouragement and good advice, we would like to thank everyone who has been involved with *VocalChoices* in pilots, INSETs, trying out the exercises, reading through the manuscript and finally getting it published. We would like to thank especially:

Liz Meek, Headteacher, and Rhona Millar, Head of Music, at Addington School; Craig Battams, Principal, St. Patrick's Special School, Adelaide, South Australia; Mary Jacquier, Principal, Our Lady of La Vang School, Adelaide, Australia; the staff and pupils of Addington School, Reading, Berkshire, Kennel Lane School, Bracknell, Berkshire, Castle School, Newbury, Berkshire, Our Lady of La Vang School, Adelaide, South Australia and St. Patrick's Special School, Adelaide, South Australia; colleagues on the Sounds of Intent Research Team at the Institute of Education, University of London: John Brockhouse, Margaret Cork, Birgitta Ferron, Dr Evangelos Himonides, Pat Lloyd, Professor Adam Ockelford, Peggy Penfold, Jane Rusch, Sue Simmonds, Sally Zimmerman; Dr Evangelos Himonides for help with the PAS2 and PEVOC6 *VocalChoices* posters; Dr Jan Švec for advice about dosimetry; Mary Chapman, Judith Ellis, Liz Harley, Mel Mehta, Sally Rogers and Susan Martineau for reading the manuscript and giving invaluable suggestions; Maria Clarkson, Lynda Chitty, Dr Lesley Hendy, Ursula Somers and Jade Wheldon for help and encouragement; Noel McPherson at Compton Publishing for seeing the potential and helping to make it happen; an extra big thank you to Professor Graham Welch who has championed and encouraged our project from the beginning; and above all thanks to our families and friends for their constant support especially Laurence, Matthew and Reuben McNaughton and Natalie, Alfred and Claribel Kemp.

Further acknowledgements for drawings and photos

The drawings that accompany these vocal exercises were inspired by Matt's work with his pupils at Addington School, Reading, Berkshire, UK.

We wish to acknowledge with grateful thanks the outstanding contributions of Mollie Wallace, Ben Rivers, and Thomas Alford and their parents for kind permission to use the drawings.

We also wish to acknowledge the pupils and parents of St. Patrick's Special School and Our Lady of La Vang School, Adelaide, South Australia for kindly allowing us to use photographs of pupils doing the exercises and our thanks to Megan Rogerson for taking them.

The drawings and photographs greatly enhance the quality and impact of the work described in this book.

Liz McNaughton and Matthew Kemp

Foreword

It is a great pleasure and an honour to be invited to provide a foreword for this exciting new book. Everyone needs help from time to time in keeping their voices healthy and this is especially the case for those whose career activities embrace a significant vocal threat from extensive voice use, i.e. those who rely on their voice as a 'tool of trade'. Amongst those whose voices are under the greatest physical threat are teachers. They represent one of the largest groups that attend voice clinics, both in the UK and elsewhere, globally. This is because of the specific physical demands that are made on our voices in classroom and equivalent settings. Being able to keep our voices healthy is an essential component in our effective communication to support the learning of others. This excellent book provides a series of deceptively simple exercises that have been designed (and proven) to keep teachers' voices healthy whilst, at the same time, allowing them to share this physical maintenance in enjoyable and motivating ways with their students. Everybody benefits! The physical and vocal exercises are underpinned by the latest international voice protection science and collectively represent an extremely welcome new toolkit for teachers. I commend the book to anyone who is working as a teacher in an educational setting. You will have much fun in protecting your voice and the voices of your students at the same time. We owe Liz and Matt a great debt for sharing their expertise and successful experience in such an accessible and beautifully illustrated text. This is a must-read book for everyone in teaching, not just those in music!

Professor Graham Welch, PhD MA BEd(Hons) CertEd
Established Chair of Music Education, UCL Institute of Education, University College London
Chair, Society for Education, Music and Psychology Research (SEMPRE)
President, International Society of Music Education (ISME) (2008-2014)

Preface

I hear and I forget. I see and I remember. I do and I understand.
Confucius

When we started to put this book together, we were aware of the difficulties many teachers experience keeping their voices healthy. It has been well known for a long time. Unfortunately, in spite of the best efforts of many voice care specialists, there has never been enough education and training on the importance of voice care in the teacher training toolkit. This book is a contribution to that toolkit.

Many of the schemes that have been put in place to help teachers involve a great deal of paperwork, questionnaires, feedback sheets, meetings and waiting for training. At best the schemes are patchy countrywide in the UK, at worst non-existent. Our aim was to put something in teachers' hands that they could use straight away in the classroom, not just for themselves but also for their pupils: simple exercises that would raise awareness and put a warm-up process in place which, if done regularly, could have a significant impact on keeping voices healthy and functioning well.

Mostly, we take our voices for granted until they do not work and then the first sign of trouble comes as a shock especially if it threatens our livelihood. Although we do not often realise it, doing a warm-up before we start the teaching day is as necessary for us as vocal athletes as it is for sports athletes. Like brushing our teeth every day, twice a day, vocal exercise needs to be done regularly and often. We would not put off brushing our teeth for two weeks, so we should not put off doing vocal warm-ups daily to protect our voices.

In order to put our ideas into practice, we started in the SEN arena as that is where Matt teaches. However, when introducing the exercises to a mixture of SEN and mainstream teachers at the Institute of Education, University College London, in the Celebrating Music INSET days over several years (2004–2009), it became clear from the many requests received that we needed to open up the exercises to everyone teaching in primary, secondary and FE education in the UK and even further afield.

So while the exercises started life as applicable to those in SEN education, we now believe they are a useful tool for anyone working in the classroom in groups or one-to-one teaching in the English-speaking world. In the future, through translation, our hope is that they will reach other countries as well. The problem of vocal wellbeing is a global one. We hope our book will really help to prevent problems and improve teachers' and pupils' voices everywhere.

Liz McNaughton and Matthew Kemp

Introduction and background

Music education in schools

It is widely recognised by teachers and other professionals and affirmed in the UK Department for Education document *The Importance of Music* (2011) that music and communication skills play an important part in all education, including special needs education.

This vocal skills package came about as a result of working with a music specialist in special needs education. However, as the project has progressed and developed over several years, it has become clear that it has a general application in mainstream education as well, and not only in a musical context but also in terms of voice use generally. It also has a place in the vocal education of other countries, particularly but not exclusively in the English-speaking world.

However, let us go back to how the whole project began.

Vocal education in SEN schools

According to the Department for Education and Skills in 2003, there were 1471 SEN schools in the UK. While working in this area of education, the Authors noticed a gap in special needs provision which their work aimed to fill by introducing a vocal foundation package that could be used for the benefit of pupils and teachers alike.

An initial pilot at Addington School in Reading, UK, had demonstrated that such an approach could be very beneficial for pupils in promoting vocal development, coordination skills and social awareness as well as supporting the healthy voice use of their teachers.

According to UK government statistics for 2002–2003, there were approximately 1.4 million pupils with special educational needs, and in the Provision of Music in Special Education (PROMISE) report (2001), it had been shown that provision of music education was satisfactory or better in only a third of SEN schools. This suggested, therefore, that the quantity and quality of provision was very variable and particularly neglected in the area of vocal education. There had been little or no input in voice development and, arguably, there was a great need for more to be done.

Since then the picture has not changed significantly as far as vocal health education is concerned but the numbers of special needs schools, after an initial rise, have now fallen again due to the inclusion of many pupils with special needs and disabilities in mainstream schools. The government numbers for 2016 show that there are 1039 SEN schools in England and a further 222 in the rest of the UK. Pupil numbers have reduced and are now approximately 1.2 million.

It should be noted that from September 2014, SEN is now known in the UK as SEND. (See *Key to acronyms* on p.85).

Benefits of vocal education generally

As well as the benefits it brings to music and drama specifically, the benefits of working with the voice in general are physical, cognitive, emotional and social.

Voicework helps to improve postural alignment and cardiovascular activity as well as pulmonary function through aerobic exercise. The work also helps individuals to develop self awareness and awareness of others and therefore enables them to relate more closely to the world around them.

It addresses the quality, breadth and relevance of learning for young people by introducing and testing new approaches to teaching and learning providing foundation work of a lasting nature. It has the potential to improve motivation and behaviour that promotes the pupils' emotional and social development. In special needs education in particular, it makes learning more accessible and relevant for young people across the learning difficulty range - MLD, SLD, PMLD, ASD, ADHD and other syndromes.

Taking everything into consideration, we decided to undertake this work after consulting Professor Graham Welch of the Institute of Education, University College London, who confirmed that this was indeed still a neglected area of music education within the special needs provision. We were then linked to the work of the PROMISE research team at the Institute which was looking into the area of music in special education.

Vocal health of teachers

At the same time, we were also aware of the situation regarding the state of vocal health in the teaching profession across the whole of the UK. Of the 500,000 or so teachers in the UK, many are at risk and frequently absent from work with vocal problems and, according to the Voice Care Network UK, 'Effective use of voice and skills in oral delivery are vital elements in children's education and in classroom management.'

This is echoed by Sir John Cullen, former Chair of the Health and Safety Commission's Schools Education Advisory Committee (SEAC) when he said, 'A strong and healthy voice is essential for teachers to do their job effectively.'

The largest teachers' union in the UK, the National Union of Teachers, has expressed concern about occupational voice loss as it is reckoned that one in five teachers has time off work for a voice-related problem in any given year. Moreover, this is not just recognised in the UK. When we began working on this project in 2003, there was already a massive interest in occupational vocal health problems particularly in the teaching profession. Such interest led eventually to the first International Conference on Occupational Voice Research in 2007 in San Antonio, Texas and to a wealth of research projects looking into the problem. Surprisingly, however, even now in 2016, apart from small pockets of voice care training, all the indications that prevention is so much better than cure still have not led to the inclusion of voice training as a compulsory and vital ingredient in overall teacher training in the UK or, it seems, anywhere else.

The result is that vocal problems persist in the teaching profession. Teachers are given advice but not necessarily a simple way of implementing that advice. Many trainee teachers may have at best one hour of information about how to look after their voices but with little actual functional experience of the exercises that could make a great difference to their vocal wellbeing and therefore to their ability to teach effectively and confidently.

It is reckoned that at least 50% of teachers will have some kind of vocal problem during their teaching career costing the educational purse huge sums in lost teaching days, teaching cover and treatment costs. In fact, in a report by Katherine Verdolini and Lorraine Ramig in 2001, they reckoned that this situation costs the USA alone $2.5 billion annually. The picture does not seem to have changed appreciably in the intervening years.

Research shows that the problems of teachers' vocal wear and tear and voice loss are reported worldwide in North America and Canada, Latin America, Australasia, Northern and Southern Europe, Africa, the Middle East and East Asia as well as in the UK. Examples of research papers are listed in the *Bibliography* for further reading.

The message is always the same however big or small the research sample: teachers represent a small percentage of the overall population but an enormously high proportion of people presenting at voice clinics with vocal problems. There tends to be a greater number of women but this may also reflect that there are usually a greater number of female teachers in the profession, especially in the primary and special needs sectors.

Dosimetry

Recognising that the vocal wear and tear on teachers' voices is a worrying aspect of teacher health and therefore the ability to teach, has led to finding a way of measuring the wear and tear in a quantifiable format. This research can then be used to help in assessing and alleviating the damage.

This has been achieved by using dosimetry in which a small device is attached to the teacher's neck which can record the number of cycles the vocal folds make during the teaching day. The results are surprising and shocking as it has been calculated in one study looking at a teacher's high occupational voicing percentage that almost 1.6 million vocal fold collisions occurred on average for female teachers and about 1 million for men during approximately 7½ hours of teaching. Put another way, according to the research done by Dr Jan Švec and others, in recording the vocal dose of an administrator, the distance covered by his vocal folds was almost 3 km per 12 hours with the voicing percentage of about 14%. In teachers, the doses and voicing percentages appear to be about double. It is no wonder that teachers are on the 'at risk' list in voice clinics.

Using this information brings home, not only to teachers themselves but also to the authorities who require them to work without any formal voice training, why teaching is one of the most vocally demanding occupations. In turn, this has led to teachers being able to back up claims brought against their employers in cases where occupational vocal damage has caused them to be off work for long periods of time or, worse still, to be unable to return to work at all.

Effect of the teaching voice on pupils' learning capability

Another important aspect of vocal health care is research that shows that a teaching voice with problems, or dysphonia, affects the ability of pupils to learn properly. A dysphonic voice is one with impaired phonation, for example hoarseness or roughness, which undermines interest and confidence in the teacher and what he or she is talking about and therefore renders learning outcomes far less effective.

There are various studies which show the importance of this information and which give a further argument for addressing vocal problems as a matter of urgency. For example, in 2005 Jemma Rogerson co-authored a paper in the *Journal of Voice* in which she asked 'if dysphonic teachers' voices have an effect on children's processing of spoken language'.

The answer was emphatically that they do, as it results in poorer listening and processing of what is being said. It also highlighted the fact that there was no difference between a mild or severely dysphonic voice; they both had a detrimental effect on the learning process.

It was concluded that any form of vocal impairment is detrimental to children's speech processing and is therefore likely to have a negative educational effect. Because of the high level of vocal impairment in the teaching profession, this research added weight to the urgent need for the implementation of specific voice care in this area. Similar findings have been recorded in other studies in the UK and in Sweden.

Two further factors

Along with the recognition of the vocal problems teachers experience in their working lives, it is important to mention two other factors which need to be taken into consideration. The first is the amount of noise created in a school not just by the pupils and the teachers, but also by the acoustics of the building and other ambient noise. The second is the legal implications of teachers having to work without adequate training and support from their school and local education authority.

- ### *Noise in schools*

  There is no doubt that schools are noisy places but the fact of the matter is there are ways in which noise can be cut down. Unfortunately, these involve expense but this has to be weighed against the cost of covering or replacing a teacher, or paying substantial damages for inadequate help for teachers affected by the noise whether direct or ambient.

  To this end, Environmental Protection UK and the Institute of Acoustics have a Noise Action Week every year and in 2011, focused particularly on schools. In the pamphlet *Noise and Your School*, they point out that too much noise affects learning by disrupting long-term memory, impairing reading ability and affecting concentration. Noise also adds to teacher stress and voice strain and interrupts classes generally.

  They think, therefore, that it is vital for schools to include noise management and reduction in all their operational planning and strategic thinking for improving the school environment. This means looking at what can be done with existing schools but also making sure that new buildings take these factors into consideration.

Among the important factors that they list for consideration are: minimum acoustics standards for schools according to Section E4 of Building Regulations; designing classrooms with 'good' acoustics that support inclusive learning and are protected from noisy areas; and designing external teaching areas that are protected from noise.

Environmental Protection UK is a leading national charity set up to provide expert analysis, advice and advocacy on noise as well as other matters affecting the environment in which we live and work.

The Institute of Acoustics is the UK's professional body working in acoustics, noise and vibration and is a nominated body of the Engineering Council.

- ***Legal implications of voice problems***

As has already been mentioned, if the damage to teachers' voices is very severe, it can mean that they have to be off work for considerable periods of time while undergoing treatment and voice rest. It may even mean that they are unable to return to work at all as their voices will never be sufficiently robust to manage the strenuous task of teaching full-time.

In this situation, it has now been established in several important cases that there may be a cause for compensation, and there have been a number of successful tribunals where teachers have been awarded substantial damages for loss of work due to unsatisfactory teaching conditions.

One of the biggest payouts was in 2010 when a teacher successfully claimed against her local authority which maintained that voice problems were an occupational hazard that went with the territory. The teacher was awarded £156,000 in an out-of-court settlement but she has never taught again.

It is, therefore, most important that employers are made aware of the potentially huge financial implications of ignoring the training and support of their staff which is necessary if they are to avoid such situations. For more information see the TUC's article *Work hoarse* in their health and safety magazine *Hazards* published in 2004 and listed in the *Bibliography*.

Scope of exercises

It is our hope, therefore, that through these exercises, we can raise awareness and encourage vocal activity that will help to address this problem in some way. We also hope that it will not only work physiologically and in non-musical aspects of development, but will also enhance individual musical imagination through preparing the singing voice and also, by regularly exploring the voice, help to develop a sense of personal identity – both for pupils and their teachers.

It is intended that the package can be applied to cover all ages, genders and ethnic groups within the SEN and mainstream school communities, both primary, secondary and FE, and will benefit these groups by developing their physical, cognitive, social and emotional lives. It is also designed for use by non-specialist music coordinators and their staff as well as music specialists.

Speech, language and communication difficulties are among the most common problems in remedial education and specially trained teachers or visiting speech and language therapists are frequently required to deal with them. Through this work we hope to provide a means of delivering general vocal self-help for teachers that will benefit and enhance the social and communication skills of the whole school.

It can also act as a bridge for teachers between speech and language therapists and music therapists and in some way ease their heavy work load, not as a replacement but as a useful supportive tool.

Initial case study data supports this hypothesis and further research is ongoing. The major development that has come out of piloting the package and presenting it at INSET days is how much it could benefit teachers and pupils across the whole of the education spectrum. It is for this reason that we have moved from our initial plan to serve SEN education specifically to open the whole package to mainstream education as well.

Developing the exercises

How it all started

In 2003, Matt went to Liz for help with his voice, particularly his singing voice. As a music specialist, he was experiencing some problems due to the vocal wear and tear of a heavy teaching schedule in a busy school. They worked together on basic exercises for both speaking and singing and very soon Matt felt a great improvement in his voice.

As has already been mentioned in the *Introduction and background*, it is important to emphasise that it is very common for teachers to have voice problems (formally recognised by the then DfES in their health guidance) and teachers are the largest professional group attending ENT and speech therapy clinics in Europe and North America.

At the time, Matt was Head of Music at Addington School, Reading, UK, which became, under his guidance, the first special needs music college in the UK. When Matt subsequently used the same exercises with his special needs pupils in his own music teaching at school, he noticed a marked improvement in their vocal health and ability as well. Other teachers also noticed that their pupils were more alert in class after this voicework and expressed an interest in knowing more about the vocal exercise activities.

Development of the package

As a result, it was decided to structure a vocal exercise package more specifically so that other colleagues could use it. A pilot package of 20 key exercises and explanations was put together for regular use in the school timetable to help not only the pupils' vocal ability and health but that of their class teachers as well.

The package consists of linked complementary exercises that cover posture and relaxation, articulation and resonance, and breathing. It can enhance the school day by giving teachers a 'toolkit' to use as an aerobic warm-up/warm-down for class routines, stimulating or calming both in group and individual situations.

The underlying intention for the whole project is to raise awareness about what can be done through voicework to improve and maintain the voice and provide a foundation for using the voice in a healthy and effective way, whether for speaking or singing for pupils and their teachers. These key activities involve a series of exercises to be done on a regular basis, combining vocal skills with whole body movement.

Piloting

The exercises were successfully piloted in two special schools. Pupils were from UK Key Stage 1 (ages 5 to 7) to FE (post-16, non university) level with ability ranging from PMLD to MLD, often associated with autistic spectrum disorders. They were also trialled over several years (2004–2009) at the Celebrating Music INSET days at the Institute of Education, University College London.

It was at these CPD days that the teachers attending decided the package would be very useful in mainstream classes as well as in those for special needs pupils.

A video demonstrating the exercises as a teaching reference accompanies this explanatory book. Medium and short versions of the exercises are provided in case of shortage of time in the teaching day. These can be downloaded according to need from the website link.

The exercises are a useful teaching aid for teachers at any time of the school day. They can be done standing, sitting and even lying down with some adaptation. They can be used by all ages, genders and ethnic groups.

As stated previously, the benefits are physical, cognitive and emotional, and help bring about better communication socially as well as laying good foundations vocally. Pulmonary function, aerobic efficiency and cardiovascular activity can all be improved as well as awareness of self and others.

Further recognition

The exercises have been presented at international voice conferences at the National Center for Voice and Speech in Denver (Physiology and Acoustics of Singing PAS2 2004) and at the Royal Academy of Music, London (Pan-European Voice Conference PEVOC6 2005). In 2007, they were accepted as part of the Department of Health and the Arts Council of Great Britain's publication *A Prospectus for Arts and Health*.

Postscript

Matt left Addington School in August 2008 to embark on a family adventure to Australia. In his new city of Adelaide, South Australia, he quickly found work at Our Lady of La Vang School and St. Patrick's Special School (Catholic Special Schools Incorporated).

For five years Matt developed the music programmes at both schools and enabled the students to share their unique musical talents at the prestigious annual Catholic Schools Music Festival, held at the Adelaide Festival Theatre.

While in Australia, Matt continued to use the *VocalChoices* exercises himself, with staff and, of course, with as many students as he could.

In 2014, Matt returned to the northern hemisphere with his young family, living and working in Jersey, Channel Islands. He continues to work in SEN education at Mont à l'Abbé School. *VocalChoices* is still a regular warm-up for Matt and he has had no further vocal problems since implementing the exercises on a regular basis.

The vocal apparatus: a simple overview

The exercises in this book enable teachers to access a simple vocal workout easily. They cover the basic requirements for warming up the voice, ready for speaking or singing.

The remit of the book is to give a handy way of accessing safe and easy exercises that will stimulate or calm and always help to keep voices healthy.

There are a great many medical and scientific articles and research books on voice which go into the detail and these should be referred to for further information. See the *Bibliography* for suggested reading.

Anatomy

There are three ingredients necessary for making vocal sound:

- the vocal folds or cords
- the vocal tract
- the breathing apparatus

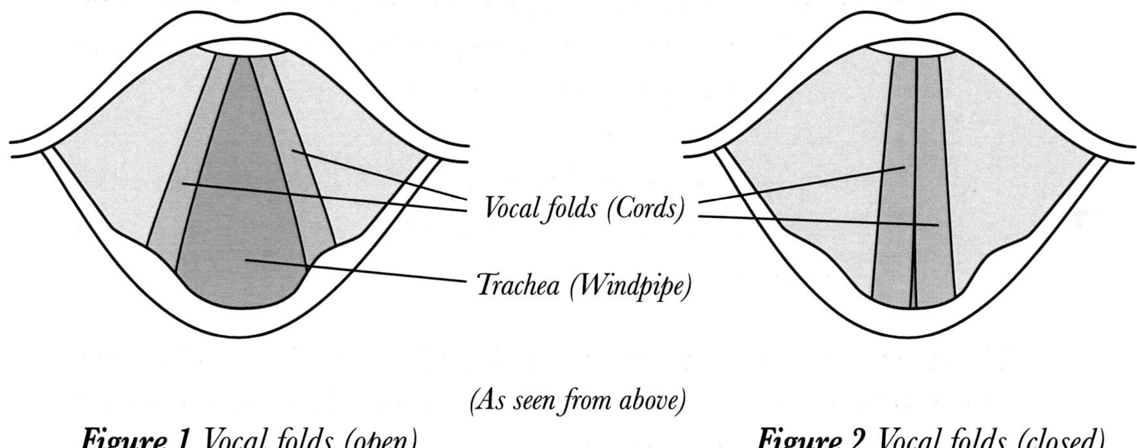

Figure 1 *Vocal folds (open)*

Figure 2 *Vocal folds (closed)*

The vocal folds represent the vibrator that is necessary for making sound whether spoken or sung. They are situated in the larynx and made up of thin pieces of muscle with a system of layers that keeps them durable and supple.

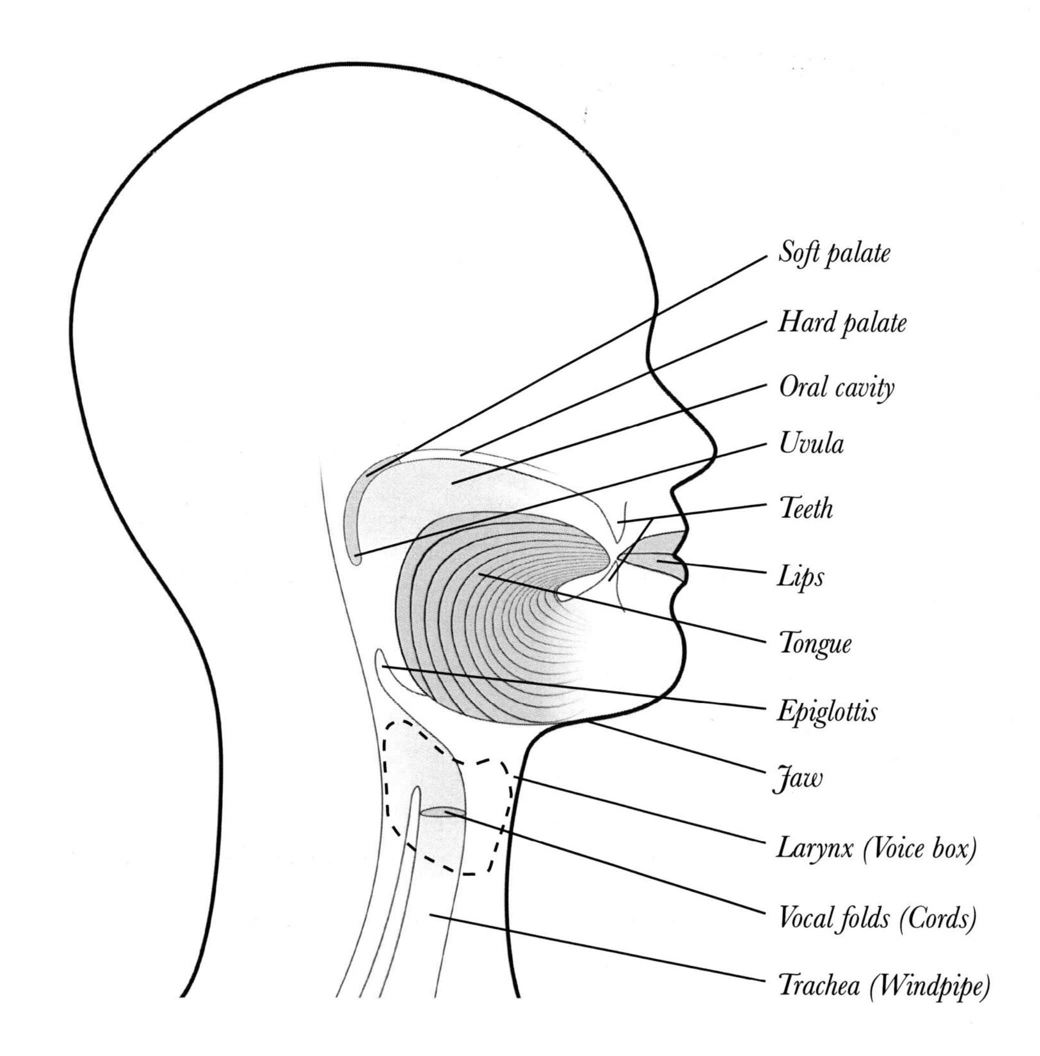

Figure 3 *Simplified view of the vocal tract and articulation system*

The vocal tract is the oral cavity and mouth which includes the lips, tongue, soft palate and jaw. It acts as a resonator after the air passes through the vocal folds.

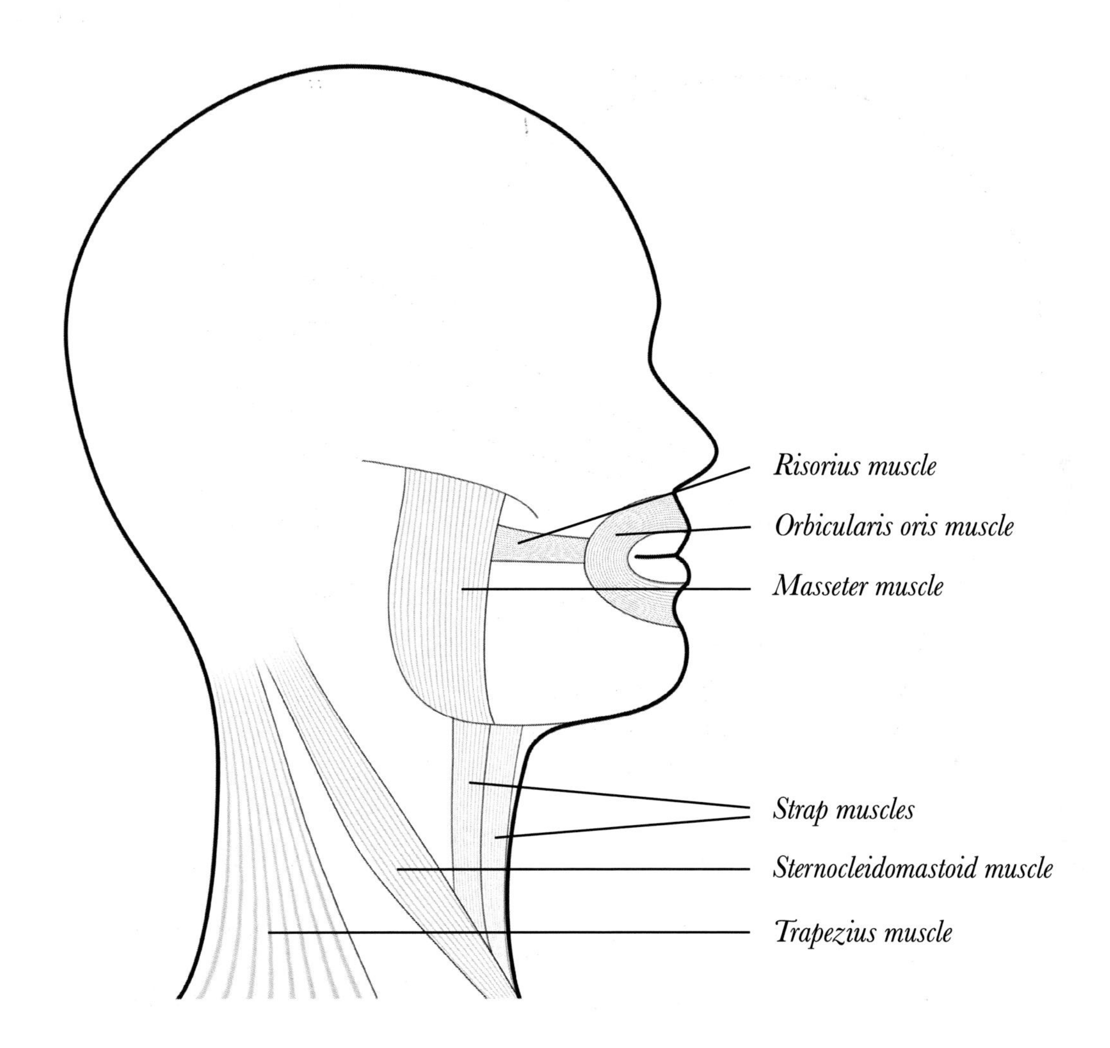

Figure 4 *Simplified view of the face and neck muscles that need to be warmed before voicing*

The trapezius, sternocleidomastoid and strap muscles help support the larynx. The masseter (jaw), orbicularis oris (kissing) and risorius (smiling) muscles are part of the resonance and articulation system.

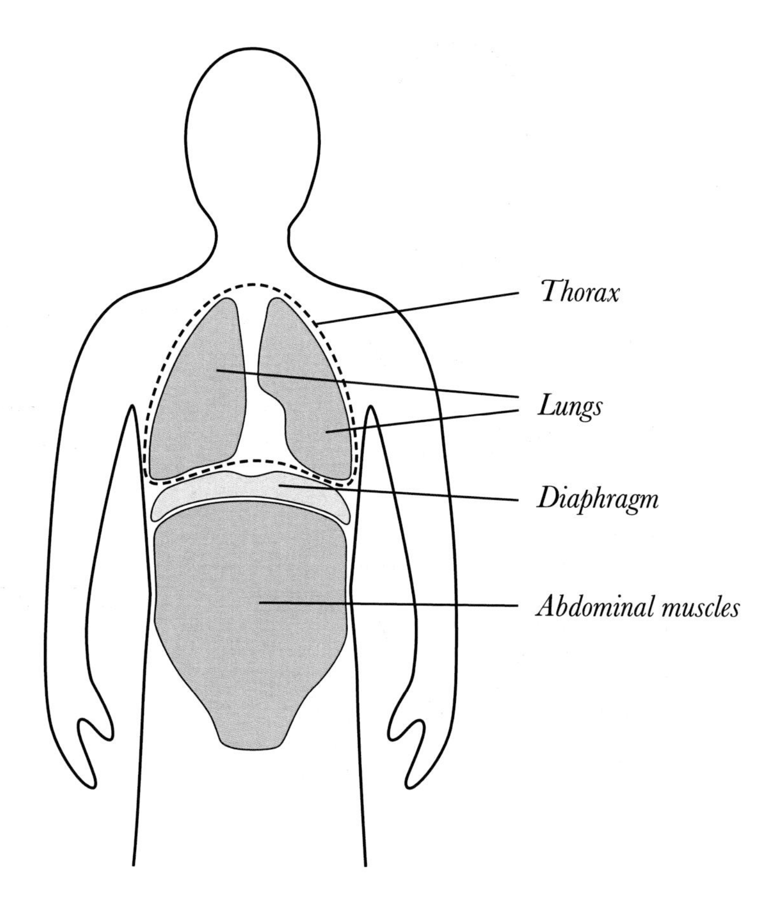

***Figure 5** Simplified view of the breathing apparatus (front)*

The breathing apparatus consists of the lungs, rib cage, intercostal muscles, diaphragm, and back and abdominal musculature. It provides the energy or fuel for the voice.

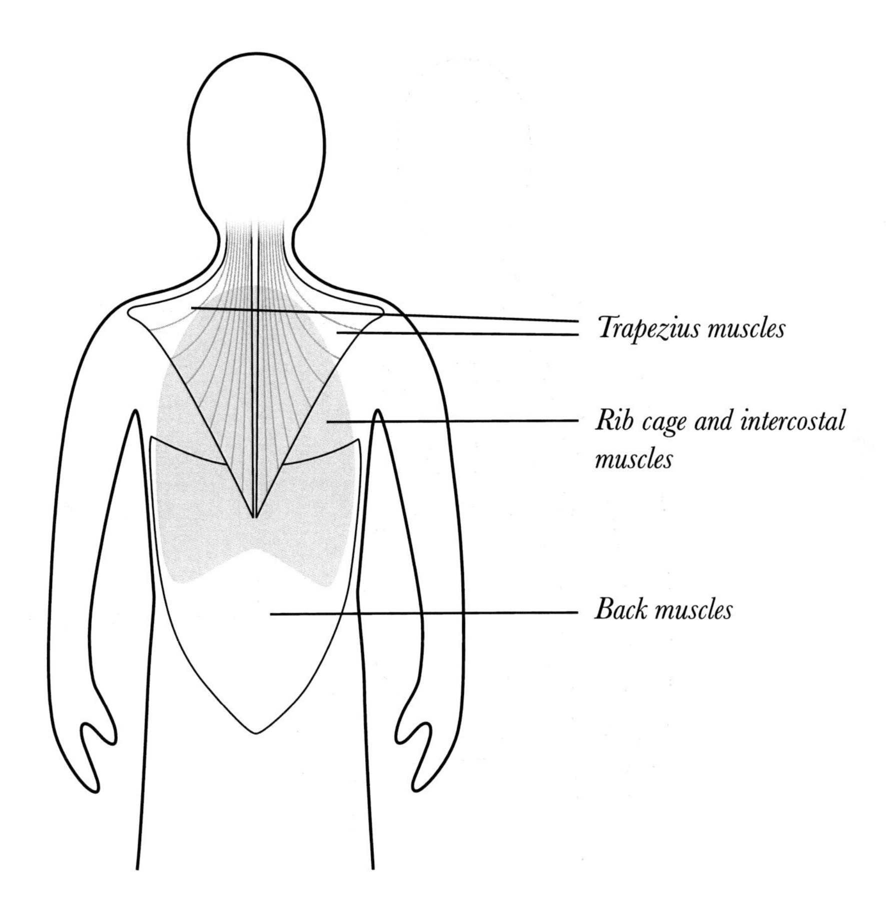

Figure 6 *Simplified view of the breathing apparatus and trapezius muscles (back)*

The rib cage houses the lungs; the intercostal muscles consist of three layers which are used for inspiration and expiration. The diaphragm is a dome-shaped muscle which provides a flexible division between the thorax and abdomen and is incapable of sensation.

As far as is known, it is impossible to control the diaphragm independently. We just know that it has to be working (like the heart) and that we can make it work more effectively by using the extremely important muscles of the abdomen more efficiently.

Physiology

This concerns the function of all three parts of the vocal anatomy as described above.

The lungs supply a constant stream of air that passes between the vocal folds. This is achieved by the workings of the intercostal muscles along with the diaphragm and abdominal musculature.

Although there are many different theories about breathing, it is generally agreed that on inspiration, the diaphragm descends and pushes the abdominal organs downwards and forwards, allowing air to fill the enlarged space made available in the lungs. On expiration, the whole process is reversed and the abdominal muscles work in harmony to push the abdominal contents against the diaphragm. This causes it to relax and rise, and the expanded lungs and enlarged rib cage to diminish.

As the airstream from the lungs reaches the vocal folds, they start to vibrate so that they open and close very quickly. The muscular control of the vocal folds is extremely complex and involves several muscle groups working in coordination to lengthen and thin the folds for high sounds and then to shorten and thicken them for low ones. Through this process we are able to vary the pitch and tone of our voices. It is amazing to consider that if, for example, the human voice is making a sound at a frequency of 440Hz, which is equal to A above middle C, the vocal folds will be opening and closing 440 times per second.

When the air leaves the vocal folds, it makes a buzzing sound and it is only when it enters the resonating spaces of the oral cavity that we get a full sound and it becomes possible to alter this sound into different shapes, tone qualities and dynamics. By utilising the articulation system of tongue, lips, soft palate and jaw, it is then possible to make the focused sounds required in speaking and singing.

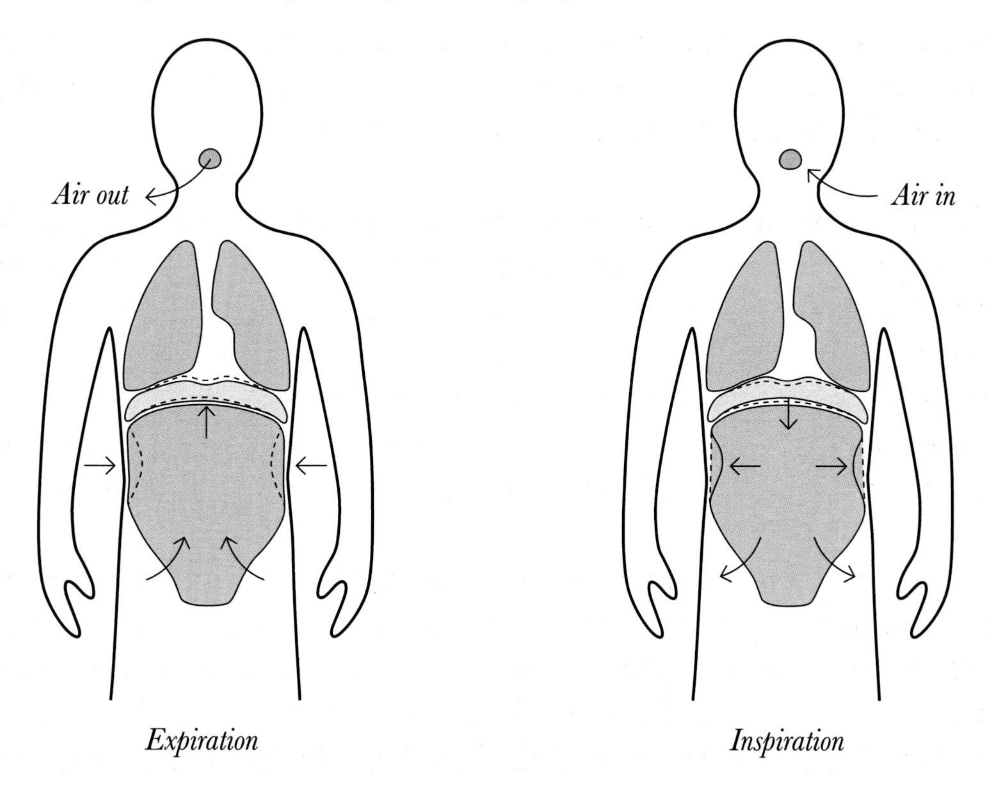

Figure 7 *Simplified view of muscle movement during breathing process*

A closer look at the 20 exercises and the rationale for choosing them

The exercises are planned so that each main area of physiological activity is addressed. The exercises can be done standing, sitting and, in some cases, even lying down. We suggest that they are done standing as far as possible but with some groups we recognise that this will not be possible.

The exercises may have to be modified for pupils with special educational needs but, as the pilots have shown, nearly all pupils can manage to achieve some improvement in vocal ability.

Exercises 1–7

Whole body posture, release and balance

In order for the vocal and breathing apparatus to function properly, attention needs to be paid to the posture and alignment of the body so that everything is in balance and there is an awareness of any unnecessary tensions or lack of appropriate muscle use that may interfere with that balance.

Even where pupils have special educational needs and physical problems, it is possible to adapt the exercises and gain small improvements with regular and appropriate guidance.

Students who need to remain seated can still be helped to achieve the best body balance in a sitting position.

All this may be difficult to monitor in large class groups but if teachers and classroom assistants are aware of what to look for, they can gradually help to adjust muscle positions and therefore improve posture over time.

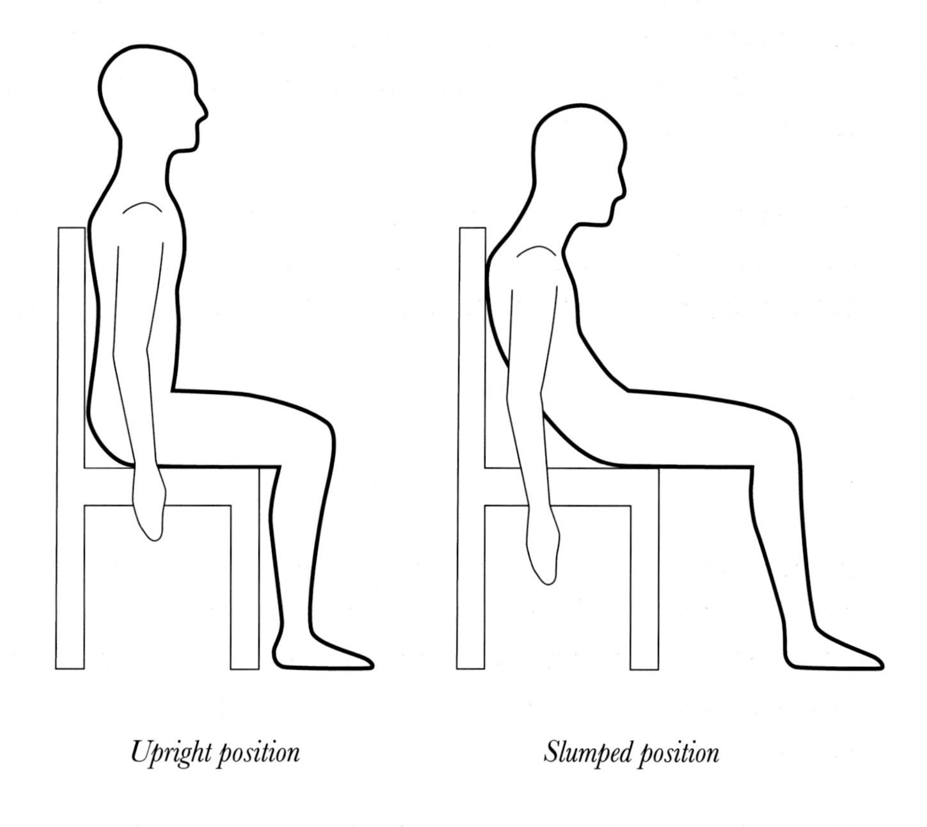

Figure 8 *Sitting posture showing efficient (upright) and inefficient (slumped) position for voicing*

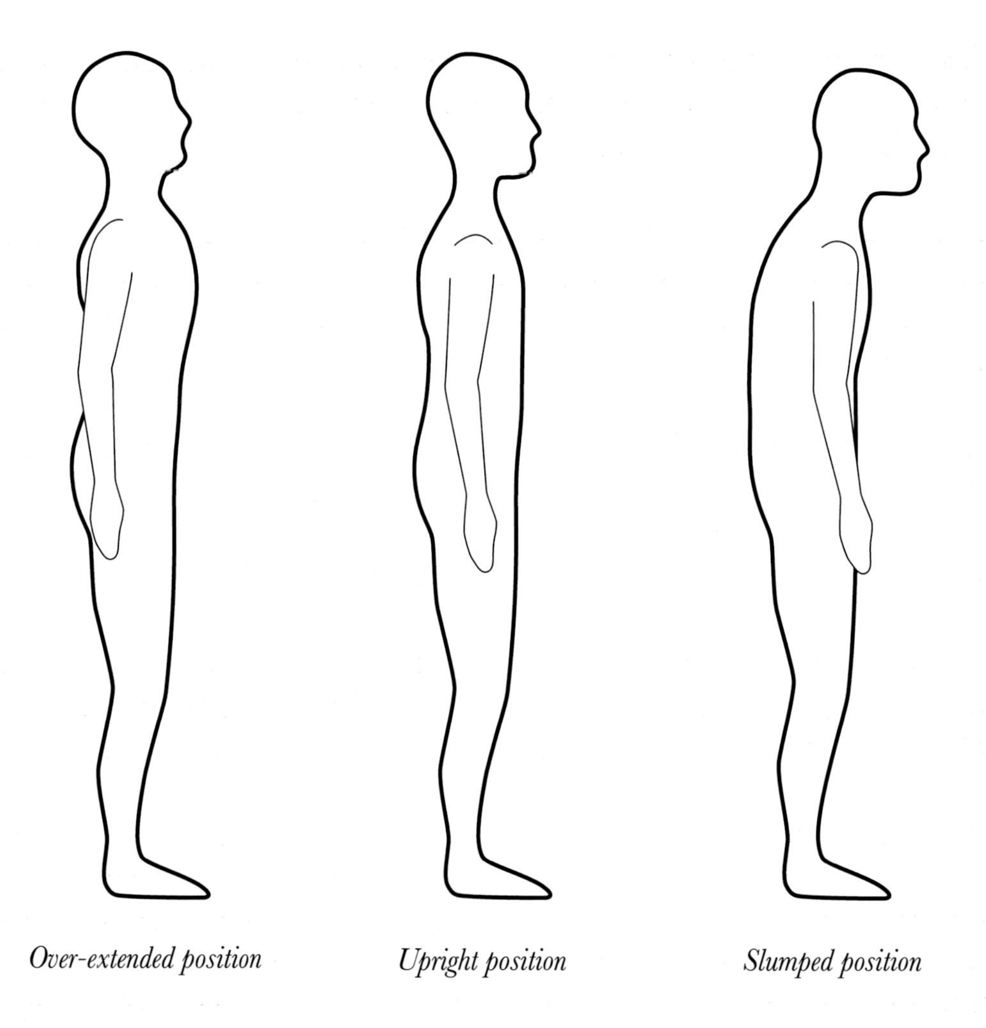

Figure 9 *Standing posture showing efficient (upright) and inefficient (over-extended and slumped) positions for voicing*

They need to work on lengthening the body and neck and getting everyone to imagine being lifted up gently by a string from the crown of the head like a puppet.

Exercises 1–4 address areas (hands, feet, shoulders, head and neck) that can hold an excess of tension. The aim, through awareness, is to put them back into better balance.

Exercise 3 is particularly good for easing the trapezius muscle (see *Figs. 4* and *6* pp.19, 21) and starting to open the chest and back for a freer rib cage and therefore making more space for the lungs and more efficient breathing.

Exercise 4 works on releasing the strap and sternocleidomastoid muscles in the neck (see *Fig. 4* p.19). Get the pupils to ask questions as well.

If possible, it is good for everyone to stand for Exercises 5, 6 and 7.

Exercise 5 encourages a really open body position with everything stretched as far as possible including ribs, even if pupils need to remain seated. It also includes the yawn-sigh for releasing jaw tension and breath.

Exercises 6 and 7 encourage complete relaxation of the body in a flopped, forward position, making sure the head and arms are released downwards, and that there is no holding of the breath. The slow return to upright position is essential in order to avoid a head rush or dizziness. The neck and head should be the last part to return to upright position. Yawning and sighing can also be used to keep the breath moving.

'Soft' knees (*Ex. 6* p.44) means that they are not locked which can put a strain on the lower back when bending forward.

It is important not to rush any of these exercises and thereby create new unwanted tensions, dizziness or hyperactivity.

Exercises 8–14

Articulation and resonance

These exercises focus on getting the articulation system working: jaw, tongue, lips, soft palate, and introducing some vowels and consonants.

They can be used to enhance communication between teacher and pupil and pupil and pupil, developing eye contact and body language.

Exercise 8 concentrates on getting the jaw released by a chewing movement which grows larger and more exaggerated. The masseter muscle (see *Fig.4* p.19) is one of the strongest muscles in the body and keeping it too tight means that other articulators, like the tongue root and soft palate, are also too tight. This inhibits free muscle movement throughout the articulation set-up and therefore inhibits free and flexible sound-making, whether spoken or sung.

Introducing number counting while still maintaining a relaxed jaw requires specific coordination of the muscles and helps to check that the jaw is remaining released enough for clear sounds and words. Counting out loud helps to maintain this muscle balance. Days of the week and months of the year can also be used as well as other languages.

Exercise 9 The tongue is an extremely versatile and essential part of the articulation system, having many pairs of coordinating muscles that enable us to change its shape and make sounds in many languages. It needs to be as flexible as possible and its position in the oral cavity whether high or low, forward or back, is an essential factor affecting the clarity and resonance of our voices.

Tongue trills are a good way of exercising the tongue but may be very difficult for some pupils and their teachers, so a better option is this exercise which encourages tongues to be flicked in and out at different speeds. They can also be stretched and pointed up and down and from side to side.

Exercise 10 Lip trills may also be tricky for some pupils and teachers but are well worthwhile working on as they bring the airflow and air pressure together without putting too much pressure on the vocal folds. They also bring the sound forward on to the lips and make it more difficult to constrict the throat.

They help to encourage a wider pitch range and when the hand movements and knee release are added in, this aids whole body coordination keeping a healthy muscle balance throughout the entire system and taking unnecessary pressure off the vocal equipment.

Exercise 11 works on the back of the tongue and the soft palate and encourages a smooth glide throughout the pitch range. It is also a safe way of lengthening and shortening the vocal folds. Adding in the coordinating arm and knee movements also makes the exercise more effective, as in *Exercise 10*.

Exercises 12–14 involve the orbicularis oris (kissing) and the risorius (smiling) muscles (see *Fig. 4* p.19).

Exercise 12 introduces vowels and diphthongs in a memorable sequence with the /m/ consonant as a strong springboard for the sounds. It helps with clear lip shaping and the use of different pitches. To keep it clear, aim for a more 'twangy' sound.

'Twang' is defined as a bright, piercing sound produced by having the tongue high in the mouth and pressing the sides of the tongue against the sides of the top teeth. It can be achieved by making cat sounds as in the 'miaow', a witch's cackle or lambs bleating. A great many cartoon voices make use of the 'twang' and it is certainly a very useful voice quality for teachers to cut through noisy classroom sounds, or across playing fields and swimming pools. It is safe to use and will help to protect and preserve the voice in difficult acoustic spaces.

Exercises 13 and 14 both help to explore resonance of the voice through rich vowels sounds and clear consonants as well as adding in a social element which can be used to develop class communication through a story with body movement and eye contact. Coordination is again an important element of these exercises.

Exercises 15–19

Connecting up the breath

These exercises are for getting the breathing connected up with the sound using the abdominal muscles as far as possible, leaving the chest and shoulders relaxed and using the fricatives /s/, /sh/ and /z/ to produce a steady controllable sound. Mouth breathing is recommended with an active out breath using abdominal tension and a passive in breath using abdominal release.

This use of the abdominal muscles is vital if counterproductive pressure is going to be removed from the vocal muscles so that they are free and flexible to make sounds easily. For this reason, there are several variations on this theme which really train the muscles to engage and coordinate for healthy voice use.

We need the breathing apparatus to be used in a balanced way which means the breath needs to be controlled from low down in the body with the help of the strong abdominal musculature. This in turn helps to move the diaphragm more efficiently which then brings pressure to bear on the lungs and enables the air to flow through the vocal folds with the right subglottic air pressure for voicing.

Exercise 15 gets to grips with the importance of the abdominal muscles in the breathing process. By making a clear connected sound like dogs barking high and low, everyone should be able to feel the muscles engaging and releasing in between barks.

Exercise 16 continues the theme of getting in touch with the breath connection. This time it is with a softer sibilant /s/ sound which still keeps the connection real when feeling the muscles of the tummy. The name of the exercise also contributes to the enthusiasm of the pupils doing it as they imagine the hissing snakes.

Exercise 17 again works on this vital connection using /sh/ and without putting too much strain on the vocal folds. It encourages everyone to work on varying the length of the breath by introducing the idea of being at the seaside with small waves (short strong breaths) or great big waves (long steady breaths getting louder at the end) really making the abdominal muscles work.

Exercises 18 and 19 introduce louder, more connected sound but still in a safe way, bringing the folds together by using the fricative /z/ and 'whoo' sounds. These again are good for varying the breath length and encouraging coordinated body movement. Both breathing variations feed the imagination as sounds and breath become connected and everyone is focused on being bees and ghosts!

Exercise 20

Warm down into neutral

It is important to leave everyone in a safe, neutral place after experiencing what may have been a busy, fun, and probably very noisy exercise time. The aim is for everyone in the classroom to be ready and focused for the next task of the day.

Exercise 20 brings everything together in a final stretch, yawn, sigh and hum. It should not be hurried and, if possible, there should be a moment of quiet at the end. Pupils and teachers should be calm, contented and ready to move on with a voice that is much more able to address healthily the daily vocal work load.

VocalChoices: The 20 key exercises

The exercises fall into three sections:

Whole body posture, release and balance

01. Handy Hands and Shimmy Shake
02. Foot Stomper
03. Shoulder Roller
04. Heady Heads
05. Sunrise Stretch
06. Rag Doll Flop
07. Slow-motion Snail

Articulation and resonance

08. Toffee Time and Counting
09. Baby Babbling
10. Motor Mouth
11. Sirens
12. Miaow
13. Me and You
14. Funny Fireworks

Connecting up the breath

15. Big Dog, Small Dog
16. Hissing Snakes
17. Seaside Sounds
18. Buzzing Bees
19. Haunted House
20. The Big Yawn

01.

Handy Hands and Shimmy Shake

Method: shake and stretch hands, shake and shimmy shoulders and move hips in loose, easy way.

Explanation: releases tension in hands, fingers and thumbs as well as in shoulder girdle, pelvis, knees and ankles - all of which can get locked in one position.

releases tension throughout whole body

Watch out!
Encourage everyone to make some kind of movement but be careful that those who have more mobility don't get over-enthusiastic!

'shake...
...stretch'

02.

Foot Stomper

Method: running feet on the spot and stop. This can be done sitting or standing.

Explanation: good for energising feet and legs, and increasing blood flow and better breathing; coordinates and controls muscles used to stop and start movement.

energises feet and legs, coordinates and controls muscles

Remember!
Even those in wheelchairs can do small movements in a sitting position.

'Stomp...
...and
stop!'

03.

Shoulder Roller

Method: raise shoulders up to the ears and then drop fully, releasing breath at the same time. Then roll shoulders slowly forward three times and back three times, also releasing the breath.

Explanation: relaxes shoulders that can get fixed and painful. Forward and backward movements help mobility and relaxation across the shoulder girdle, which in turn releases tension in the vocal muscles and also helps to open up the chest and back.

releases tension in shoulders, gives lungs more space for breathing

Watch out!
No breath holding! Make sure everyone releases their breath as much as possible while they do the exercises.

‘r-o-u-n-d’

04.

Heady Heads

Method: keeping shoulders still, say 'yes' (nod head) and 'no' (shake head) in answer to questions asked by the teacher, for example: 'Do you like chocolate?' 'Do you like spiders?'

Explanation: works on neck muscles in two different directions; questions encourage interaction and cognitive skills, as well as flexible head and neck movement.

helps flexibility in neck muscles and social interaction through questions

Watch out!
See they don't get over-enthusiastic with delicate neck muscles and raise their heads too high - we don't want pulled muscles!

Yes
No

05.

Sunrise Stretch

Method: reach up into a big stretch with semi-circular arm movements, add a yawn and sigh as the arms are lowered.

Explanation: this extends the area of body movement, opens up the ribs for breathing more efficiently and helps to release tension in the upper body.

stretches and frees upper body

Watch out!
See there is enough space around pupils otherwise they will hit each other!

's-t-r-e-t-c-h'

06.

Rag Doll Flop

Method: keeping knees 'soft', bend over gently, flopping head and arms, and releasing shoulders and breath with a big sigh.

Explanation: allows body to release fully and encourages release of back in every direction. This exercise leads into Exercise 07.

helps to release back, shoulders and neck

Watch out!
See that everyone releases neck muscles fully by letting head go, otherwise there will be a strain on the larynx which is counterproductive.

'flop!'

07.

Slow-motion Snail

Method: continuing from Exercise 06, uncurl very slowly to upright position, keeping the breath moving all the time.

Explanation: this slow movement is to achieve maximum release, allowing the body to return to an upright position, feeling more lengthened and balanced.

extends and balances body safely

Watch out!
It's really important to leave the chest, shoulders, arms, neck and head to the very last - be on the lookout for any speedy customers as they could end up with a head rush or dizziness.

's-l-o-w'

‘1, 2, 3...’

08.

Toffee Time and Counting

Method: make jaw chewing movement while counting - you can pop some imaginary toffees in your mouth to help with the chewing and counting!

Explanation: releases tension in jaw, especially good if you can start with a small movement and get gradually bigger. Keep chewing and count slowly from 1 to 5 and back again - some teachers do this in French, for example (or any other language), to help language skills as well.

keeps jaw flexible

Watch out!
Make sure everyone continues the jaw movement when they start counting - otherwise the jaw can become frozen with concentration.

'blah blah blah'

09.

Baby Babbling

Method: flick tongue in and out, fast and slow.

Explanation: this exercises the muscles of the tongue and releases tension, especially in the tongue root.

keeps tongue flexible

Watch out!
Mind the flying spittle!

'brrr...'

10.

Motor Mouth

Method: *do car and motorbike lip trills at different pitches plus hand and knee movements up and down.*

Explanation: *keeps sound forward and connects up airflow and air pressure in correct balance without putting too much strain on the vocal folds or causing the throat to constrict. By adding in hands and knees, it keeps coordination of body, mind and voice.*

promotes good balance between breath and body

Watch out!

You need moist lips to get started and see that as far as possible everyone keeps an upright posture rather than leaning forward which puts pressure on the larynx and prevents good body alignment.

ng........ng........ng

11.

Sirens

Method: making ambulance, fire engine and police car sounds plus hand and knee movements.

Explanation: making sounds on 'ng' (as in 'sing'), gliding up and down the pitch range brings together the back of the tongue and soft palate.

exercises vocal folds safely and encourages smooth pitch range

Watch out!
Keep the jaw released during sirening - a tight jaw will create unnecessary tension in the tongue root.

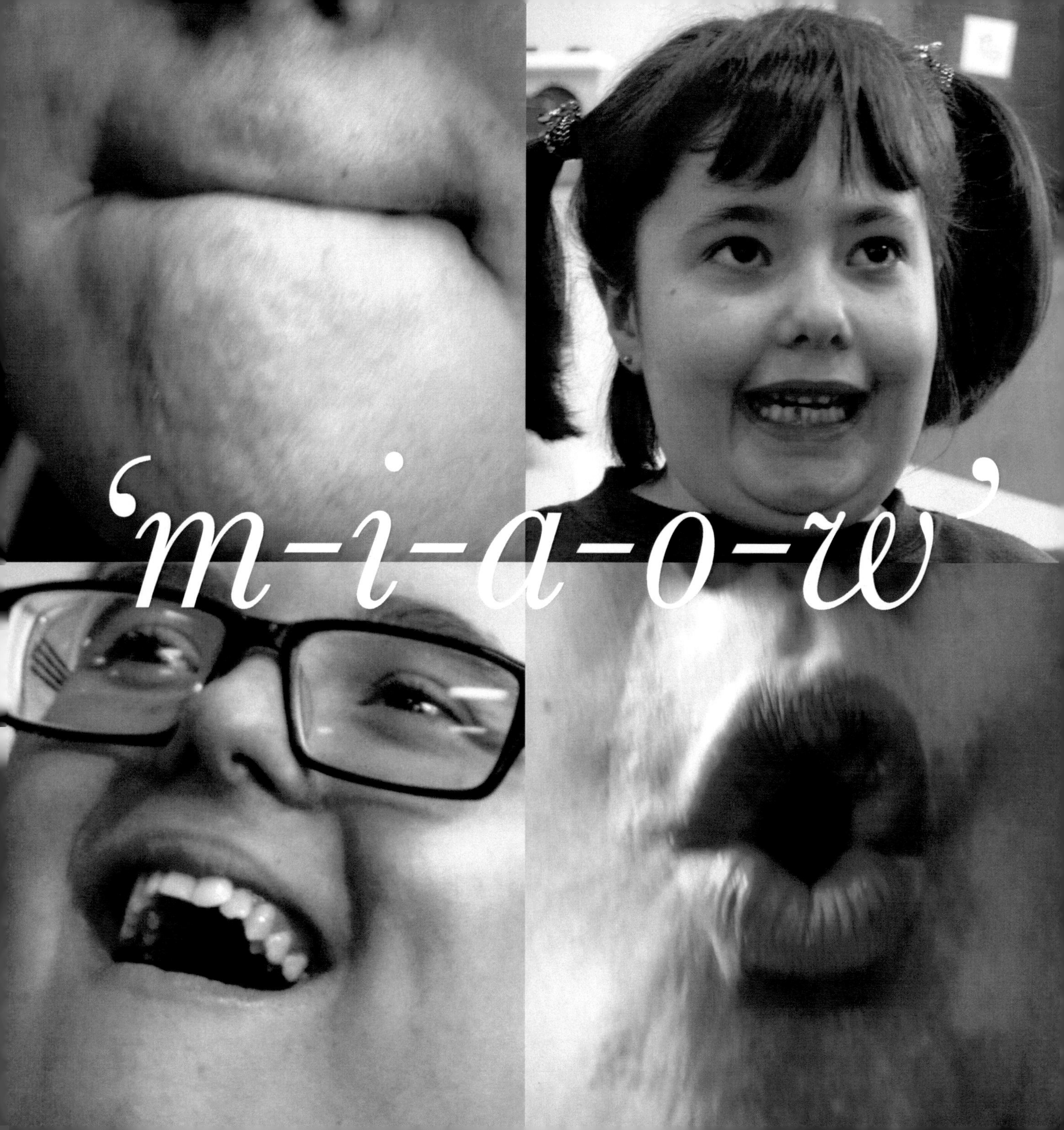
'm-i-a-o-w'

12.

Miaow

Method: do exaggerated long cat's 'miaow' sound at different pitches.

Explanation: works on lip muscles for vowel shaping and encourages big, bold vowel and diphthong sounds: ee-eh-ah-ow.

encourages clearly articulated sounds

Watch out!

Keep sounds clear and 'twangy' - no croaky cats allowed! For more information on 'twang' *see p.30.*

'ee...
...oo'

13.

Me and You

Method: speak the words 'Me' and 'You' with long extended vowel sounds while pointing at each other.

Explanation: this again encourages clear articulation and resonance using lips fully; also encourages interaction between pupils and teacher, with eye contact and coordination of the body through hand movements and pointing at each other.

works on resonant sound and body language

Remember!
Some may feel it's rude to point, but it's very good to encourage eye contact and group interaction through a controlled exercise.

‘oooh...
ahhh...
...wow’

14.

Funny Fireworks

Method: Make 'ooh!' sounds on the way up, then 'ahh!' or 'wow!' on the way down plus hand movements.

Explanation: allows a bigger, freer, more resonant sound, and introduces an emotional dimension through ideas of anticipation, excitement, pleasure or disappointment.

introduces resonant sounds with emotional dimension

Watch out!
Hand movement brings in whole body coordination so the exercise works on several levels. Keep an eye on the body alignment where necessary: too much leaning in will put unnecessary pressure on the larynx.

15.

Big Dog, Small Dog

Method: placing hands around the body on waist and abdomen, make 'big dog' barks at low pitch and 'small dog' barks at high pitch.

Explanation: enables everyone to feel muscular connection in the body to sound-making activity, and works on pitch range and onset of the sounds as well.

works on connecting body and breath at different pitches

Watch out!
Some people may get too enthusiastic! Can become very noisy which is difficult for those with sensitivity to loud noise - still well worth doing for working on connections in the body.

'woof woof'

16.

Hissing Snakes

Method: make short and long sounds on 'sss' using hand movements as well as putting hands on tummies.

Explanation: enables a steady flow of air to be achieved and controlled through use of the abdominal muscles.

works on developing steady airflow

Watch out!
That flying spittle again!

‘ss...ss...
...sssssss’

17.

Seaside Sounds

Method: make sounds like long and short waves on the beach to 'shh' plus hands on tummies.

Explanation: another way of controlling breath flow and feeling connection to muscular activity in the abdomen.

continues strong, steady and controlled airflow

Remember!
This introduces the possibility of a story about a day at the beach with sound effects!

shshshshs

18.

Buzzing Bees

Method: make long and short 'zzz' sounds plus hands flying around like bees in flight.

Explanation: uses a fricative /z/ to introduce more vocal sound into the airflow - requires control with starting and stopping sound on long and short breaths.

introduces control of steady sound with airflow

Watch out!
Check that the sound is as steady as possible on the long buzz - this will tell you how stable the connection is between airflow and air pressure.

‘zzzZZZZ’

19.

Haunted House

Method: make ghostly 'whooo' sounds at different pitches, with ghostly hands.

Explanation: free flowing sound at different pitches, quite soft like wind in the trees or in a tall chimney, accompanied by soft flowing hand and arm movements. This enables a steady sound to be developed which does not put too much pressure on the vocal folds, but helps to warm up the voice.

connects sound and movement safely at different pitches

Watch out!
The ghosts may get too loud!

20.

The Big Yawn

Method: have a big stretch and long, long yawn and sigh, moving down into a contented hum to finish.

Explanation: final opportunity to stretch and release muscles before getting on with the next school task - sighing and humming allows the voice to warm down after all the previous activity and takes it into a neutral position of rest.

leaves voice safely warmed and focused

Remember!
There should be nothing to watch out for now - everyone should feel calmed or stimulated ready for the next task of the day and with a voice ready to work:

Happily, safely and effectively!

'ahhh...
...mmm'
ST PATRICK'S
SPECIAL SCHO

Tips for doing the exercises

Using the video and exercise templates

The video is available from www.vocalchoices.com and has a demonstration of all 20 exercises.

There are also downloadable colour-coded templates of the exercises available on this website. We suggest that teachers may like to keep a record of progress made by their pupils and also to monitor their own voices as well.

It is our intention that teachers only use the video in order to see how the exercises work and, if this is a completely new activity, to give them the opportunity to practise so that the exercises can be introduced to pupils in the classroom with complete confidence.

While it may be useful to show the video to a class or on a one-to-one basis from time to time, it is important that teachers do the exercises with their classes to get the vocal practice themselves. This not only protects their own voices but helps to facilitate the social and communication element of the exercises with their pupils. Merely playing the video in class will not allow this to happen and will be a lost opportunity in the building of vocal stamina, muscle memory and confidence for both teacher and pupil.

The video is also useful as a staff training tool. The exercises can be used widely in the school timetable by any member of staff as an essential resource in order to raise awareness about the importance of looking after your voice whether you teach music or maths, PE or chemistry.

If further help is needed to train teachers in basic voice care skills through CPD workshops, these can be arranged in the UK. (See www.phoenixagain.com for further details.)

Keeping records

We are sure that each school will have its own method of keeping records and we encourage teachers to track how their pupils are doing with the exercises, to see if there are any improvements in vocal stability and strength, and also for the teachers to monitor their own vocal health and exercise regime.

Reports from the pilot studies were very useful in helping us choose the most effective exercises. Some presented more difficulties than others, some were enjoyed more than others, but all of them produced a vocal result which was beneficial in some way.

Some exercises are necessarily noisier. For lots of pupils this made them more fun but for some pupils, particularly those on the autistic spectrum, this presented a challenge. Overall the response was one of enjoyment and many of the pupils said that they felt good at the end of the sessions.

When there isn't enough time to do all the exercises

It is possible that, although all the exercises can be completed in approximately 15 minutes, this may seem to be too much to fit into a busy school timetable.

For this reason, and to give teachers a choice, short and medium versions are also suggested. There are three different templates of the exercises which each still fall into three sections, all incorporating the main elements of stretching and releasing tension, waking up the articulators and resonance, and connecting everything through steady breath control via the abdominal musculature.

The shorter versions are only a guide to help teachers at the beginning, and in time we are sure they will choose the ones they wish to do. We would just like to suggest that exercises are always chosen from each of the three colour-coded sections so that there is a proper balance of postural, articulation and resonance, and breathing exercises in the mix.

Obviously, we realise that teachers and pupils will have their favourites but we want to encourage the use of all the exercises over time. Repetition and regularity are key factors in any exercise regime and if all 20 exercises are addressed in this way, maybe even more can be added in gradually as well.

Having said that, one of the most important points to remember is that it is no good rushing through all the exercises just to get them completed. They must be done at a steady pace with awareness of the reasons for doing them. It is better to do a few at a time and do them well.

This leads the way to everyone gaining confidence, strengthening the muscle memory and maintaining better vocal health and efficiency in the long run.

Variations on a theme

Of all the exercises that are available to us as vocal practitioners, we have chosen the ones that seemed to be the most popular and give the best possible outcome for our pupils and their teachers in terms of vocal health, efficiency, general ability and having fun. This last element is, we believe, very important in any learning situation when dealing with diverse moods, states of health and commitment to the task.

As the exercises become familiar, it is a good idea to encourage pupils to lead an exercise. If teachers find they can use their own creative skills and develop variations from these exercises which help them and their pupils to do more vocally, then we are very happy to have acted as a catalyst for this vital part of the teaching and learning continuum.

Tips for when your voice doesn't work

Many of the problems that can beset the voice are functional rather than pathological and can be prevented or rectified by regular vocal exercise such as those recommended in this book. However, sometimes the voice succumbs to other forces: an extra heavy vocal load (e.g. too many hours teaching), infection, environment or diet.

Some of the common difficulties teachers experience are the result of a gradual build-up of problems which become chronic, or those that appear suddenly, as in the case of a cold or laryngitis.

Common complaints:

- hoarseness
- roughness
- having a dry mouth
- having a tight throat
- having a sore throat
- constant throat clearing
- constant dry cough
- excessively breathy voice
- feeling vocally tired
- running out of breath
- voice fading out by the end of the day, week, term

Other common issues to take into consideration

Laryngitis: recurring laryngitis usually results from lack of sufficient voice rest to clear the initial problem. Antibiotics are not the answer unless a test is done to check whether it is bacterial laryngitis. This is comparatively rare. Most problems persist because sufferers continue to work with the condition.

Reflux: acid reflux is very common and can cause redness and burning of the vocal tract as acid and gases from food and drink consumed return up into the laryngeal area. It requires a visit to the doctor for investigation and possible medication. Certain foods cause more problems than others, e.g. spicy foods, chocolate, tomatoes, acidic fruit juices. Eating late and stress are also possible causes.

Asthma: for many people, this is a chronic condition requiring regular daily medication. It is essential that enough water is taken with the medication to prevent dehydration, and possibly the use of a spacer. It is also suggested that improving breathing technique helps: if the abdominal muscles are more engaged, this can help lower the high-chested breathing common in many asthmatics and therefore remove some of the pressure put on the vocal muscles.

Immediate ways of alleviating the problem

Water: drink at least 6-8 glasses a day, maybe more in hot weather but certainly, in the words of the distinguished American laryngologist Van Lawrence, aim to 'pee pale'. Sips rather than gulps.

Steam: relaxing, soothing. Do it in the evening when you can relax after work. Electric steamers are available as well as a simple steamer or a bowl of hot water and a towel over the head. Make sure the water is hot but not boiling. Do not add anything to the water e.g. menthol or eucalyptus oil, as these are also dehydrating.

Swallowing instead of constant throat clearing: try swallowing gently rather than clearing the throat vigorously as this brings the vocal folds together too energetically and exacerbates the problem. Sirening on 'ng' is also a useful way of clearing the throat.

Rest: always make sure you have enough good sleep.

Suck bland lozenges for a sore throat: e.g. glycerine and honey. Avoid very strong medicated pastilles as they may numb the throat before the problem has been resolved.

No numbing throat sprays: many are available but masking the problem will only prolong it and probably make it far worse.

No aspirin: sometimes recommended as a gargle but to be avoided as aspirin can cause vocal fold haemorrhage.

No whispering: whispering will not help if you have laryngitis. In fact, it will make things worse. Just rest your voice as much as possible. If you have to speak, use only a quiet conversational tone. Sip water and steam.

Stress: avoid stressful situations as far as possible as these can add to laryngeal tension.

Factors that may be causing the problems

Remember you are the expert on your body but here are some factors to monitor and see whether they are affecting you.

Food: dairy foods can make mucous stickier leading to throat clearing; chocolate and hot spicy food can cause acid reflux especially when eaten late at night. Leave at least 2 hours between eating and bedtime.

Drink: alcohol, tea, coffee, acidic fruit juices, fizzy drinks can all cause dehydration and reflux.

Environment: spaces that are noisy, dry, dusty, too hot, too cold, have airborne irritants such as fumes, can all have an impact on the voice and affect its performance. Problems may not be caused just by how you use your voice at school. They may also be worsened by what you do in your private life such as socialising in noisy pubs and clubs, straining your voice over loud music, or talking on the phone for long periods, especially if you clamp the phone between your head and shoulder. This tilts the head to one side and alters the laryngeal alignment.

Medication: most medications are dehydrating so make sure you have enough water with them.

Smoking: definitely very bad as it dries the vocal folds and can lead to serious disease of the vocal equipment. No excuses!

Recreational drugs: these burn at a higher temperature than ordinary tobacco so can cause tenderness in the vocal tract.

How to help yourself

Warm-up: always do some form of warm-up at the start of the day, even if it just a shake, stretch, yawn and sigh coupled with a lip trill or siren up and down the vocal range. Do it either at home e.g. in the shower or at school with your class, or both.

Warm-down: do a gentle sigh plus downwards 'oo' and hum at the end of the teaching day or at home.

Vocal load: cut down on the amount you use your voice. Get your pupils to share some of the vocal work. Try not to speak against lots of background noise. Use some kind of aural cue to give instructions to your class: beat a drum, shake a tambourine, strike a triangle, use a rainstick – anything which gives your voice a break.

No shouting: if you must shout, make sure you connect your voice to the abdominal muscles so that they take the strain and use 'twang' (see 'twang' under *Ex.12* p.30). If you can refrain from shouting, or only use it sparingly, so much the better. Watch that you don't shout at home either!

Amplification: there are many forms of amplification available for teachers in the classroom. This can give some temporary relief but should only be used as a last resort as it interferes with the direct interaction between teacher and pupils. It may allow teachers a little respite if they are having ongoing vocal problems. Remember, however, that it does not remove the need to do a vocal warm-up and exercise: it only alleviates the problem, it does not solve it. Every teacher's goal should be to return to good unamplified vocal health as soon as possible.

Professional help

Get a referral from your doctor: if problems persist for more than three to four weeks, see your doctor and get a referral to a voice clinic where there is specialist help and information, and where the multi-disciplinary medical teams are used to helping professional voice users.

Voice clinic examination: an examination by a laryngologist will lead to a diagnosis of what may be causing the problem. The best form of treatment will then be decided upon: medication, therapy, surgery, or a combination of all or some of these.

Voice therapy: this is often recommended pre- or post-operatively or if no other intervention is required. Some sessions with a speech and language therapist may be suggested followed by another voice clinic review to see what progress has been made. Further sessions can be requested if the problem persists.

Remedial speaking or singing lessons: to strengthen and maintain good vocal health after treatment. These can be delivered by a voice teacher or singing teacher experienced in rehabilitation work and who is often recommended by the voice clinic.

Always take great care of your voice - it's the only one you've got!

Key to acronyms

ADHD	Attention Deficit Hyperactivity Disorder
ASD	Autistic Spectrum Disorder
CPD	Continuing Professional Development
DCSF	Department for Children, Schools and Families (2007–2010)
DfE	Department for Education (2010–)
DfES	Department for Education and Skills (2001–2007)
ENT	Ear, Nose and Throat
FE	Further Education
INSET	In Service Training
MLD	Moderate Learning Difficulties
PMLD	Profound and Multiple Learning Difficulties
PROMISE	Provision of Music in Special Education
SEN	Special Educational Needs (from September 2014 known in UK as SEND: Special Educational Needs and Disability)
SLD	Severe Learning Difficulties
SLT	Speech and Language Therapist

Bibliography

Akinbode, R., Lam, K.B.H., Ayres, J.G. and Sadhra, S. (2014) Voice disorders in Nigerian primary school teachers. *Occupational Medicine.* http://occmed.oxfordjournals.org/content/early/2014/05/03/occmed.kqu052.short

Assunção, A. Á., Bassi, I. B., de Medeiros, A. M., de Souza Rodrigues C. and Gama A. C. C. (2012) Occupational and individual risk factors for dysphonia in teachers. *Occupational Medicine.* http://www.occmed.oxfordjournals.org/content/64/1/16.full

Chapman, J. L. (2006) *Singing and Teaching Singing: A Holistic Approach to Classical Voice.* San Diego, CA: Plural Publishing

Charn, T.C. and Mok, P.K. (2012) Voice problems amongst primary school teachers in Singapore. *Journal of Voice* 26(4) e141–e147.

Child, D. (1997) *Psychology and the Teacher.* 6th Edition London and New York: Cassell.

Cutiva, L.C.C. and Burdorf, A. (2015) Effects of noise and acoustics in schools on vocal health in teachers *Noise and Health* 17 (74), 17–22 http://www.noiseandhealth.org/article.asp?issn=1463-1741;year=2015;volume=17;issue=74;spage=17;epage=22;aulast=Cutiva

DfE *The Importance of Music: A National Plan for Music Education.* (2011) https://www.gov.uk/government/uploads/system/uploads/attachment_data/file/180973/DFE-00086-2011.pdf

Dehqan, A. and Scherer, R. C. (2013) Acoustic analysis of voice: Iranian teachers. *Journal of Voice* 27(5), 655 e17–21.

Gaskill, C. and Weems, W. (2009) Occupational vocal health: an emerging workplace wellness issue. *Occupational Health and Safety.* http://ohsonline.com/Issues/2009/07/July-2009.aspx

Harris, T., Harris S., Rubin, J.S. and Howard, J.M. (1998) *The Voice Clinic Handbook*. London: Whurr Publishers Ltd.

Hunter, E.J. and Titze, I.R. (2010) Variations in intensity, fundamental frequency, and voicing for teachers in occupational versus non-occupational settings. *Journal of Speech, Language, and Hearing Research* 53(4), 862–875.

Kallvik, E., Lindström, E., Holmqvist, S., Lindman, J. and Simberg, S. (2014) Prevalence of hoarseness in school-aged children. *Journal of Voice* (Parts of the results in the present study were presented at the 10th Pan European Voice Conference PEVOC 2013 in Prague, Czech Republic). http://www.jvoice.org/article/S0892-1997(14)00124-6/abstract

Laukkanen, A.M., Ilomäki, I., Leppänen, K. and Vilkman, E. (2008) Acoustic measures and self-reports of vocal fatigue by female teachers. *Journal of Voice* 22(3), 283–289.

Lawrence, V.L. (1986) Sermon on hydration (or, 'The evils of dry'). In Thurman, L. and Welch, G.F. (eds.) (2000) *Bodymind and Voice: Foundations of Voice Education*. Revised Edition Iowa: National Center for Voice and Speech

Lee, S.Y-Y., Lao, X.Q. and Yu, I.T-S. (2010) A cross-sectional survey of voice disorders among primary school teachers in Hong Kong. *Journal of Occupational Health* 52(6), 344–352.

Lyberg-Åhlander, V., Haake, M., Brännström, J. K., Schötz, S. and Sahlén, B. (2014) Does the speaker's voice quality influence children's performance on a language comprehension test? *International Journal of Speech-Language Pathology*. 17(1), 63–73 http://informahealthcare.com/doi/abs/10.3109/17549507.2014.898098

Martin, S. and Darnley, L. (2004) *The Teaching Voice*. 2nd Edition London and Philadelphia: Whurr Publishers Ltd.

Mattiske, J. A., Oates, J. M. and Greenwood, K.M. (1998) Vocal problems among teachers: a review of prevalence, causes, prevention, and treatment. *Journal of Voice* 12 (4), 489–499.

Morton, V. and Watson, D. R. (2001) The impact of vocal quality on children's ability to process spoken language. *Logopedics Phoniatrics Vocology* 26(1), 17–25.

National Union of Teachers (NUT) (2011) *Health and safety briefing: Voice care for teachers.* https://www.teachers.org.uk/files/voice-care_0.doc

Pemberton, C., Oates, J. and Russell, A. (2008) Voice injury in teachers: How to minimise occupational risk. *Victorian Parliamentary Inquiry into: Effective Strategies for Teacher Professional Learning.*
http://www.parliament.vic.gov.au/images/stories/committees/etc/PL_Submissions/pemberton201108.pdf

Rogerson, J. and Dodd, B. (2005). Is there an effect of dysphonic teachers' voices on children's processing of spoken language? *Journal of Voice* 19(1), 47–60.

Roy, N., Merrill, R. M., Thibeault, S., Parsa, R. A., Gray, S. D. and Smith, E. M. (2004) Prevalence of voice disorders in teachers and the general population. *Journal of Speech, Language & Hearing Research* 47(2), 281–293.

Roy, N. and Tanner, K. (2013) All talked out. Vocal wear and tear is the greatest occupational hazard for our nation's teachers. What have we learned from them? *The ASHA Leader*
http://leader.pubs.asha.org/article.aspx?articleid=1784810

Russell, A., Oates, J. and Greenwood, K.M. (1998) Prevalence of voice problems in teachers. *Journal of Voice* 12(4), 467–479.

Sataloff, R.T. (1998) *Vocal Health and Pedagogy*. San Diego, CA: Singular Publishing Group

Shewell, C. (2009) *Voice Work: Art and Science in Changing Voices*. Chichester, West Sussex: Wiley-Blackwell.

Švec, J.G., Titze, I.R. and Popolo, P.S. (2003) Vocal dosimetry: Theoretical and practical issues. In: AQL 2003 Hamburg: Proceeding Papers for the *Conference Advances in Quantitative Laryngology, Voice and Speech Research*. (CD ROM), edited by Schade, G., Müller, Wittenberg, F.T. and Hess, M. Stuttgart, Germany:IRB Verlag, p.8

Thurman, L & Welch, G.F. (eds.) (2000) *Bodymind and Voice: Foundations of Voice Education*. Revised Edition Iowa: National Center for Voice and Speech.

Titze, I.R., Hunter, E.J. and Švec, J.G. (2007) Voicing and silence periods in daily and weekly vocalizations of teachers. *Journal of the Acoustical Society of America* 121(1), 469–478.

TUC Hazards Magazine (2004) *Occupational voice loss – Work hoarse*. http://www.hazards.org/voiceloss/workhoarse.htm

TUC (2009) Korea: Most teachers suffer from occupational illnesses. *Education International* news report • *Risks* http://www.tuc.org.uk/workplace-issues/health-and-safety/risks-newsletter/risks-2009/risks-412-27-june-2009

Voice Care Network UK. (1999) *More Care For Your Voice*. Kenilworth: Voice Care Network UK.

Van Houtte, E., Claeys, S., Wuyts, F. and Van Lierde, K. (2011) The impact of voice disorders among teachers: Vocal complaints, treatment-seeking behaviour, knowledge of vocal care, and voice-related absenteeism. *Journal of Voice* 25(5), 570–575.

Verdolini, K. and Ramig, L. (2001) Review: occupational risks for voice problems. *Logopedics Phoniatrics Vocology* 26(1), 37–46.

Welch, G.F., Ockelford, A. and Zimmermann, S-A. (2001). *Provision of Music in Special Education PROMISE*. Royal National Institute for the Blind/University of London Institute of Education.

Williams, J. (2012) *Teaching Singing to Children and Young Adults*. Abingdon: Compton Publishing.

Williams, N. and Carding, P. (2005) *Occupational Voice Loss*. Boca Raton, FL: Taylor and Francis Group.

All URLs accessed May 2016 and correct at time of going to print.

Index

About the authors

Liz McNaughton, MA, LLB, is a freelance specialist teaching both the singing and speaking voice. She has post-graduate qualification in vocal education and considerable experience of helping teachers through one-to-one sessions and voice care workshops for schools, colleges, universities and teaching unions. Liz has taught singing in various colleges including the BRIT School and the Guildhall School of Music and Drama. She has been a tutor for the Voice Care Network UK, has served on the Council of the British Voice Association and as a member of the Sounds of Intent research team at the Institute of Education, University College London. Liz has presented at national and international conferences, including the USA, Sweden and Austria, and works on a referral basis with SLTs and ENT consultants offering remedial support to teachers recovering from voice problems. Liz lives in Berkshire where she runs her own voice training and coaching business, *Phoenix Again.*

Matthew Kemp, BA, PGCE, is a teacher and music specialist working in Special Education. As Head of Music at Addington School, Reading, he led a team of 12 staff, peripatetic teachers and music therapists and in 2005 the school became the first Music Specialist College in the UK for students with special educational needs. Matt was also a member of the Sounds of Intent team at the Institute of Education, University College London. He moved to Adelaide in 2009 and developed the music curriculum at two special educational needs schools. In 2014, Matt moved to Jersey, Channel Islands, to take up a post as Key Stage Manager in Mont à L'Abbé School where he has been enabling students to participate in the Eisteddfod Music Festival and other Island events. Matt is married with two young children and is learning all about vocal development in toddlers!

Quotes from teachers on VocalChoices INSET days and pilot studies:

'A very comprehensive range of exercises.'

'Lots of potential to be used in mainstream lessons.'

'Fun, useful, I enjoyed it!'

'The demonstration is clear and can free up the voice.'

'Very accessible.'

'I like the range of exercises.'

'It's straightforward and easy to follow.'

'Help for children with speech difficulties and help with concentration.'

'Great sequence of exercises.'

'Imaginative, fun ways of approaching warm-ups.'

'Great variety to choose from.'

'Children enjoyed it and learnt better with actions.'

'Activities definitely showed pupil progress and involvement.'

'Pupils remained focused and enjoyed 'voice' work.'

'Beginning the day with the project enabled pupils to focus and begin the day alert and ready to do work.'

'Definitely felt physiological benefits after doing exercises.'

'Movement plus production of sound meant more physically relaxed and therefore mentally more focused.'

'Most enjoyment and participation from the exercises that allowed most noise!'